WELSH HISTORY STORIES

THE REBECCA

JOHN EVANS

Illustrated by Clive Spong

DREF WEN

If you have ever crossed the Severn Bridge from England into Wales, you will have had to pay some money to use the bridge. This money is called a toll. Usually, when we travel by road today, we do not have to pay a toll. But things were different in Wales 160 years ago.

There were very few roads, and the roads which did exist were
toll roads. Every person and every cart or carriage which used the
road had to pay a certain amount of money. Even when a farmer
took his cattle to market, he had to pay for his animals. The money
collected by the tollgate keeper was supposed to be used to pay
for the repair of the road, to keep it in good condition.

Thomas Rees was a poor farmer who lived in the Preseli hills of Pembrokeshire in the first half of the nineteenth century. He lived in a cottage called Carnabwth, or Stone Cottage, so Thomas was known to everybody in the locality as Twm Carnabwth. Twm was proud of his house, even though to you and me it would not have looked very grand.

It had only one room with a beaten earth floor, and very little furniture. At one end of the room was a large fireplace on which his wife, Rachel, kept an old black cooking-pot, constantly simmering the flummery which the family ate every day. Above, at the other end of the room was a half-loft, which was used as a sleeping space for Twm's three children, Elizabeth, Daniel and John.

Twm grew the oats which went to make the flummery on the land around his cottage. The soil was not very rich, and to make it better, Twm scattered lime on it at planting time, so that the oats would grow stronger. Every May, like all the other farmers in the area, Twm hitched his horse to the cart and travelled to the lime kilns to buy his lime. It was a long journey, and an expensive one because of the tolls he had to pay.

He would start his journey at midnight, and hope to be back home by the next midnight, because then he would not have to pay tolls both ways on his journey. Twm also tried to avoid paying the tolls if he could by travelling along tracks and joining the turnpike road at places where there were no tollgates, but this made the journey much longer.

Thomas Bullin was a rich businessman. He became rich by renting the tollgates from the turnpike companies. In 1839, he made a deal with the Whitland Trust, which owned the road that Twm used to fetch his lime. Thomas paid the Whitland Trust £800 for the right to collect the tolls. In return, he was allowed to increase the tolls on the road. "I have to make sure that every person who uses the road pays the toll, otherwise I will never get back my £800 and make a profit," he said. He decided to build new tollhouses on the side roads to prevent farmers like Twm avoiding the tolls. He built one at Efail-wen, and put his brother, Benjamin there to make sure everyone paid.

The new tollhouse was ready just at the time when the farmers were ready to collect their lime. The farmers were very angry. They hated Thomas Bullin and his brother and thought they were deliberately doing this to catch the farmers out. Twm knew he would never be able to pay the cost of all the tolls. The lime itself would cost him two shillings and sixpence, but the tolls would cost him another six shillings! What could he do?

9

The other farmers were saying the same thing. Twm received
word that there was to be a meeting on the night of May 12th at
Glynsaithmaen farm to discuss what should be done. All the
farmers were angry. Twm was a big man, who enjoyed a fight.
He stood up and said to the crowd, "We must smash down the
gates and teach these Bullins a lesson."

As darkness was falling the following evening, a large crowd of
men gathered outside the village of Efail-wen. Their faces
were blackened so that they could not be recognised, and they
wore women's clothes. Some carried axes and saws to destroy the
gate, others hunting-horns and drums to frighten Benjamin
Bullin away.

Seated on a horse at their head was a peculiarly-dressed figure, its white eyes shining from a blackened face. It wore a petticoat which belonged to 'Big Rebecca', a woman from a neighbouring village, and it carried a rusty old sword. Everybody called this person 'Rebecca', and chanted the name as they marched off into the darkness.

Benjamin Bullin sat at his desk in his new tollhouse. By the light of a candle, he counted up the money he had taken that day. His wife was tucking up the children in their bed, when, faintly at first, he heard the sound of horns and drums floating across the fields.

Gradually, the sounds became louder. He could hear men shouting. He went to the door and peered out into the darkness. He could see shadowy figures moving in front of the gate. Then a deep voice boomed out, "Benjamin Bullin, open the gate and let my children through."

"Who are you?" retorted Benjamin. " I will not open the gate until you all pay your tolls."

The mysterious figure bellowed back, "I am Rebecca, and my children will not pay any more tolls!" And with that, the figure turned to her followers. "Down with the gate then, my children," she ordered. "It has no right to be there!"

Benjamin ran back inside, picked up his money-box, and together
with his wife and children, ran off into the night as fast as he could.
Behind them, the crowd of farmers hacked at the gate until it was
nothing but matchwood. Rebecca waved her sword in the air
and her followers replied by shouting:
"Hurrah for free laws. Tollgates free to lime kilns!"

So began the Rebecca Riots. The tollgate at Efail-wen was attacked
twice again that year, before Thomas Bullin was ordered to
remove all the new tollgates he had erected. Three years later,
the riots began again and spread throughout Pembrokeshire,
Carmarthenshire and other parts of Wales in 1842 and 1843.
Nobody ever discovered who Rebecca was. Probably there were
several different 'Rebeccas', but it is likely that the first Rebecca
was Twm Carnabwth.

Twm continued to live at his cottage, Carnabwth, where he became a regular member of Bethel Chapel. He enjoyed reading the Bible. He often turned to this verse in the Old Testament: *"And they blessed Rebecca, and said unto her, 'Thou art our sister; be thou the mother of thousands of millions, and let thy children possess the gates of those which hate them'"*.
Can you think why?

INDEX